THE OWL
AND THE PUSSY-CAT
AND OTHER VERSES

BY

EDWARD LEAR

Edited by Roberta Sewal

THE GROLIER SOCIETY INC. • NEW YORK

CONTENTS

THE OWL AND THE PUSSY-CAT

I

THE Owl and the Pussy-Cat went to sea
    In a beautiful pea-green boat:
They took some honey, and plenty of money
    Wrapped up in a five-pound note.
The Owl looked up to the stars above,
    And sang to a small guitar,
    "O lovely Pussy, O Pussy, my love,
    What a beautiful Pussy you are,
            You are,
            You are!
What a beautiful Pussy you are!"

II

Pussy said to the Owl, "You elegant fowl,
    How charmingly sweet you sing!
Oh! let us be married; too long we have tarried:
    But what shall we do for a ring?"
They sailed away, for a year and a day,
    To the land where the bong-tree grows;
And there in a wood a Piggy-wig stood,
    With a ring at the end of his nose,
          His nose,
          His nose,
    With a ring at the end of his nose.

III

"Dear Pig, are you willing to sell for one shilling
    Your ring?"   Said the Piggy, "I will."
So they took it away, and were married next day
    By the Turkey who lives on the hill.
They dined on mince and slices of quince,
    Which they ate with a runcible spoon;
And hand in hand, on the edge of the sand
    They danced by the light of the moon,
           The moon,
           The moon,
They danced by the light of the moon.

THE DUCK AND THE KANGAROO

I

SAID the Duck to the Kangaroo,
    "Good gracious! how you hop
Over the fields, and the water too,
    As if you never would stop!
My life is a bore in this nasty pond;
And I long to go out in the world beyond:
    I wish I could hop like you,"
    Said the Duck to the Kangaroo.

II

"Please give me a ride on your back,"
  Said the Duck to the Kangaroo:
"I would sit quite still, and say nothing but 'Quack,'
  The whole of the long day through;
And we'd go the Dee, and the Jelly Bo Lee,
Over the land, and over the sea:
  Please take me a ride! oh, do!"
  Said the Duck to the Kangaroo.

III

Said the Kangaroo to the Duck,
"This requires some little reflection.
Perhaps, on the whole, it might bring me luck:
    And there seems but one objection;
Which is, if you'll let me speak so bold,
Your feet are unpleasantly wet and cold,
    And would probably give me the roo—
Matiz," said the Kangaroo.

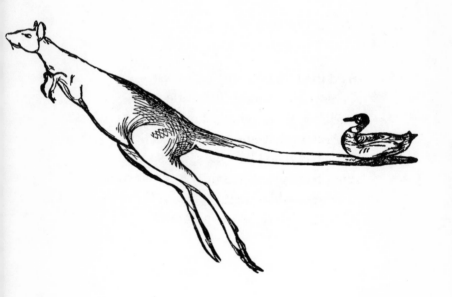

IV

Said the Duck, "As I sate on the rocks,
    I have thought over that completely;
And I bought four pairs of worsted socks,
    Which fit my web-feet neatly;
And, to keep out the cold, I've bought a cloak;
And every day a cigar I'll smoke;
    All to follow my own dear true
    Love of a Kangaroo."

V

Said the Kangaroo, "I'm ready,
    All in the moonlight pale;
But to balance me well, dear Duck, sit steady,
    And quite at the end of my tail."

So away they went with a hop and a bound;
And they hopped the whole world three times round.
    And who so happy, oh! who,
      As the Duck and the Kangaroo?

THE DADDY LONG-LEGS AND THE FLY

I

ONCE Mr. Daddy Long-Legs,
    Dressed in brown and gray,
Walked about upon the sands
    Upon a summer's day:
And there among the pebbles,
    When the wind was rather cold,
He met with Mr. Floppy Fly,
    All dressed in blue and gold;
And, as it was too soon to dine,
They drank some periwinkle-wine,
And played an hour or two, or more,
At battlecock and shuttledore.

II

Said Mr. Daddy Long-legs
    To Mr. Floppy Fly,
"Why do you never come to court?
    I wish you'd tell me why.
All gold and shine, in dress so fine,
    You'd quite delight the court.
Why do you never go at all?
    I really think you *ought*.
And, if you went, you'd see such sights!
Such rugs and jugs and candle-lights!
And, more than all, the king and queen,—
One in red, and one in green."

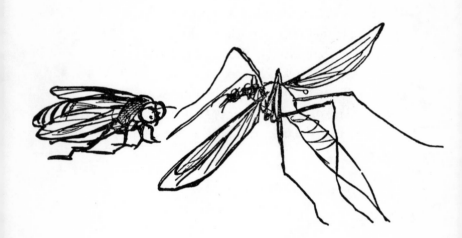

"O Mr. Daddy Long-legs!"
   Said Mr. Floppy Fly,
"It's true I never go to court;
   And I will tell you why.
If I had six long legs like yours,
   At once I'd go to court;
But, oh! I can't, because *my* legs
   Are so extremely short.
And I'm afraid the king and queen
(One in red, and one in green)
Would say aloud, 'You are not fit,
You Fly, to come to court a bit!'

"Oh, Mr. Daddy Long-legs!"
   Said Mr. Floppy Fly,
"I wish you'd sing one little song,
   One mumbian melody.
You used to sing so awful well
   In former days gone by;
But now you never sing at all:
   I wish you'd tell me why:
For, if you would, the silvery sound
Would please the shrimps and cockles round,
And all the crabs would gladly come
To hear you sing, 'Ah, Hum di Hum!' "

V

Said Mr. Daddy Long-legs,
    "I can never sing again;
And, if you wish, I'll tell you why,
    Although it gives me pain.
For years I cannot hum a bit,
    Or sing the smallest song;
And this the dreadful reason is,—
    My legs are grown too long!
My six long legs, all here and there,
Oppress my bosom with despair;
And, if I stand or lie or sit,
I cannot sing one single bit!"

VI

So Mr. Daddy Long-legs
    And Mr. Floppy Fly
Sat down in silence by the sea,
    And gazed upon the sky.
They said, "This is a dreadful thing!
    The world has all gone wrong,
Since one has legs too short by half,
    The other much too long.
One never more can go to court,
Because his legs have grown too short;
The other cannot sing a song,
Because his legs have grown too long!"

Then Mr. Daddy Long-legs
    And Mr. Floppy Fly
Rushed downward to the foamy sea
    With one sponge-taneous cry:
And there they found a little boat,
    Whose sails were pink and grey;
And off they sailed among the waves,
    Far and far away:
They sailed across the silent main,
And reached the great Gromboolian Plain;
And there they play forevermore
At battlecock and shuttledore.

THE JUMBLIES

I

THEY went to sea in a sieve, they did;
    In a sieve they went to sea:
In spite of all their friends could say,
On a winter's morn, on a stormy day,
  In a sieve they went to sea.
And when the sieve turned round and round,
And every one cried, "You'll all be drowned!"
They called aloud, "Our sieve ain't big;
But we don't care a button, we don't care a fig:
  In a sieve we'll go to sea!"
      Far and few, far and few,
        Are the lands where the Jumblies live:
        Their heads are green, and their hands are blue;
        And they went to sea in a sieve.

II

They sailed away in a sieve, they did,
   In a sieve they sailed so fast,
With only a beautiful pea-green veil
Tied with a ribbon, by way of a sail,
   To a small tobacco-pipe mast.
And every one said who saw them go,
"Oh! won't they be soon upset, you know?
For the sky is dark, and the voyage is long;
And, happen what may, it's extremely wrong
   In a sieve to sail so fast."
            Far and few, far and few,
                Are the lands where the Jumblies live:
                Their heads are green, and their hands are blue;
                    And they went to sea in a sieve.

III

The water it soon came in, it did;
 The water it soon came in:
So, to keep them dry, they wrapped their feet
In a pinky paper all folded neat;
 And they fastened it down with a pin.
And they passed the night in a crockery-jar;
And each of them said, "How wise we are!
Though the sky be dark, and the voyage be long,
Yet we never can think we were rash or wrong,
 While round in our sieve we spin."
  Far and few, far and few,
   Are the lands where the Jumblies live:
   Their heads are green, and their hands are blue;
   And they went to sea in a sieve.

IV

And all night long they sailed away;
   And when the sun went down,
They whistled and warbled a moony song
To the echoing sound of a coppery gong,
   In the shade of the mountains brown.
"O Timballoo! How happy we are
When we live in a sieve and a crockery-jar!
And all night long, in the moonlight pale,
We sail away with a pea-green sail
   In the shade of the mountains brown."
      Far and few, far and few,
        Are the lands where the Jumblies live:
        Their heads are green, and their hands are blue;
        And they went to sea in a sieve.

V

They sailed to the Western Sea, they did,—
  To a land all covered with trees:
And they bought an owl, and a useful cart,
And a pound of rice, and a cranberry-tart,
  And a hive of silvery bees;
And they bought a pig, and some green jackdaws,
And a lovely monkey with lollipop paws,
And forty bottles of ring-bo-ree,
  And no end of Stilton cheese.
      Far and few, far and few,
        Are the lands where the Jumblies live:
        Their heads are green, and their hands are blue;
        And they went to sea in a sieve.

VI

And in twenty years they all came back,—
   In twenty years or more;
And every one said, "How tall they've grown!
For they've been to the Lakes, and the Torrible Zone,
   And the hills of the Chankly Bore."
And they drank their health, and gave them a feast
Of dumplings made of beautiful yeast;
And every one said, "If we only live,
We, too, will go to sea in a sieve,
   To the hills of the Chankly Bore."
      Far and few, far and few,
        Are the lands where the Jumblies live:
        Their heads are green, and their hands are blue;
        And they went to sea in a sieve.

THE NUTCRACKERS
AND THE SUGAR-TONGS

I

THE Nutcrackers sate by a plate on the table;
  The Sugar-tongs sate by a plate at his side;
And the Nutcrackers said, "Don't you wish we were able
  Along the blue hills and green meadows to ride?
Must we drag on this stupid existence forever,
  So idle and weary, so full of remorse,
While every one else takes his pleasure, and never
  Seems happy unless he is riding a horse?

II

"Don't you think we could ride without being instructed,
  Without any saddle or bridle or spur?
Our legs are so long, and so aptly constructed,
  I'm sure that an accident could not occur.
Let us all of a sudden hop down from the table,
  And hustle downstairs, and each jump on a horse!
Shall we try? Shall we go? Do you think we are able?"
  The Sugar-tongs answered distinctly, "Of course!"

III

So down the long staircase they hopped in a minute;
 The Sugar-tongs snapped, and the Crackers said "Crack!"
The stable was open; the horses were in it:
 Each took out a pony, and jumped on his back.
The Cat in a fright scrambled out of the doorway;
 The Mice tumbled out of a bundle of hay;
The brown and white Rats, and the black ones from Norway,
 Screamed out, "They are taking the horses away!"

IV

The whole of the household was filled with amazement:
The Cups and the Saucers danced madly about;
The Plates and the Dishes looked out of the casement;
 The Salt-cellar stood on his head with a shout;
The Spoons, with a clatter, looked out of the lattice;
 The Mustard-pot climbed up the gooseberry-pies;
The Soup-ladle peeped through a heap of veal-patties,
 And squeaked with a ladle-like scream of surprise.

V

The Frying-pan said, "It's an awful delusion!"
    The Tea-kettle hissed, and grew black in the face;
And they all rushed downstairs in the wildest confusion
    To see the great Nutcracker-Sugar-tong race.
And out of the stable, with screamings and laughter
    (Their ponies were cream-coloured, speckled with brown),
The Nutcrackers first, and the Sugar-tongs after,
    Rode all round the yard, and then all round the town.

VI

They rode through the street, and they rode by the station;
    They galloped away to the beautiful shore;
In silence they rode, and "made no observation,"
    Save this: "We will never go back any more!"
And still you might hear, till they rode out of hearing,
    The Sugar-tongs snap, and the Crackers say "Crack!"
Till, far in the distance their forms disappearing,
    They faded away; and they never came back!

CALICO PIE

I

CALICO pie,
    The little Birds fly
Down to the calico-tree:
Their wings were blue,
And they sang "Tilly-loo!"
Till away they flew;
    And they never came back to me!
    They never came back,
    They never came back,
They never came back to me!

II

Calico jam,
The little Fish swam
Over the Syllabub Sea.
He took off his hat
To the Sole and the Sprat,
And the Willeby-wat:
But he never came back to me;
He never came back,
He never came back,
He never came back to me,

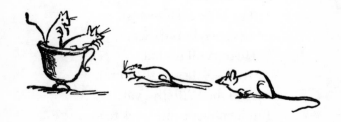

III

Calico ban,
The little Mice ran
To be ready in time for tea;
Flippity flup,
They drank it all up,
And danced in the cup:
But they never came back to me;
They never came back,
They never came back,
They never came back to me.

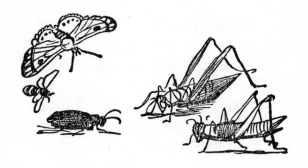

IV

Calico drum,
The Grasshoppers come,
The Butterfly, Beetle, and Bee,
Over the ground,
Around and round,
With a hop and a bound;
But they never came back,
They never came back,
They never came back,
They never came back to me.

THE BROOM, THE SHOVEL, THE POKER AND THE TONGS

I

THE Broom and the Shovel, the Poker and Tongs,
    They all took a drive in the Park;
And they each sang a song, ding-a-dong, ding-a-dong!
  Before they went back in the dark.
Mr. Poker he sate quite upright in the coach;
    Mr. Tongs made a clatter and clash;
Miss Shovel was dressed all in black (with a brooch);
    Mrs. Broom was in blue (with a sash).
        Ding-a-dong, ding-a-dong!
        And they all sang a song.

II

"O Shovely so lovely!" the Poker he sang,
    "You have perfectly conquered my heart.
Ding-a-dong, ding-a-dong! If you're pleased with my song,
    I will feed you with cold apple-tart.
When you scrape up the coals with a delicate sound,
    You enrapture my life with delight,
Your nose is so shiny, your head is so round,
    And your shape is so slender and bright!
        Ding-a-dong, ding-a-dong!
        Ain't you pleased with my song?"

III

"Alas! Mrs. Broom," sighed the Tongs in his song,
    "Oh! is it because I'm so thin,
And my legs are so long,—ding-a-dong, ding-a-dong!—
    That you don't care about me a pin?
Ah! fairest of creatures, when sweeping the room,
    Ah! why don't you heed my complaint?
Must you needs be so cruel, you beautiful Broom,
    Because you are covered with paint?
        Ding-a-dong, ding-a-dong!
        You are certainly wrong."

IV

Mrs. Broom and Miss Shovel together they sang,
  "What nonsense you're singing to-day!"
Said the Shovel, "I'll certainly hit you a bang!"
  Said the Broom, "And I'll sweep you away!"
So the coachman drove homeward as fast as he could,
  Perceiving their anger with pain;
But they put on the kettle, and little by little
  They all became happy again.
      Ding-a-dong, ding-a-dong!
      There's an end of my song.

THE TABLE AND THE CHAIR

I

S AID the Table to the Chair,
    "You can hardly be aware
How I suffer from the heat
And from chilblains on my feet.
If we took a little walk,
We might have a little talk;
Pray let us take the air,"
Said the Table to the Chair.

II

Said the Chair unto the Table,
"Now, you *know* we are not able:
How foolishly you talk,
When you know we *cannot* walk!"
Said the Table with a sigh,
"It can do no harm to try.
I've as many legs as you:
Why can't we walk on two?"

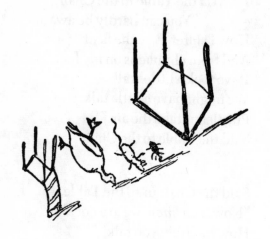

III

So they both went slowly down,
And walked about the town
With a cheerful bumpy sound
As they toddled round and round;
And everybody cried,
As they hastened to their side,
"See! the Table and the Chair
Have come out to take the air!"

IV

But in going down an alley,
To a castle in a valley,
They completely lost their way,
And wandered all the day;
Till, to see them safely back,
They paid a Ducky-quack,
And a Beetle, and a Mouse,
Who took them to their house.

V

Then they whispered to each other,
"O delightful little brother,
What a lovely walk we've taken!
Let us dine on beans and bacon."
So the Ducky and the leetle
Browny-Mousy and the Beetle
Dined, and danced upon their heads
Till they toddled to their beds.

MR. AND MRS. SPIKKY SPARROW

I

IN a little piece of wood
        Mr. Spikky Sparrow stood:
Mrs. Sparrow sate close by,
A-making of an insect-pie
For her little children five,
In the nest and all alive;
Singing with a cheerful smile,
To amuse them all the while,
        "Twikky wikky wikky wee,
        Wikky bikky twikky tee,
            Spikky bikky bee!"

II

Mrs. Spikky Sparrow said,
"Spikky, darling! in my head
Many thoughts of trouble come,
Like to flies upon a plum.
All last night, among the trees,
I heard you cough, I heard you sneeze;
And thought I, 'It's come to that
Because he does not wear a hat!'
    Chippy wippy sikky tee,
    Bikky wikky tikky mee,
      Spikky chippy wee!

III

"Not that you are growing old;
But the nights are growing cold.
No one stays out all night long
Without a hat: I'm sure it's wrong!"
Mr. Spikky said, "How kind,
Dear, you are, to speak your mind!
All your life I wish you luck!
You are, you are, a lovely duck!
　　Witchy witchy witchy wee,
　　Twitchy witchy witchy bee,
　　　Tikky tikky tee!

IV

"I was also sad, and thinking,
When one day I saw you winking,
And I heard you sniffle-snuffle,
And I saw your feathers ruffle:
To myself I sadly said,
'She's neuralgia in her head!
That dear head has nothing on it!
Ought she not to wear a bonnet?'
    Witchy kitchy kitchy wee,
    Spikky wikky mikky bee,
        Chippy wippy chee!

V

"Let us both fly up to town:
There I'll buy you such a gown!
Which, completely in the fashion,
You shall tie a sky-blue sash on;
And a pair of slippers neat
To fit your darling little feet,
So that you will look and feel
Quite galloobious and genteel.
      Jikky wikky bikky see,
      Chicky bikky wikky bee,
        Twicky witchy wee!"

VI

So they both to London went,
Alighting on the Monument;
Whence they flew down swiftly—pop!
Into Moses' wholesale shop:
There they bought a hat and bonnet,
And a gown with spots upon it,
A satin sash of Cloxam blue,
And a pair of slippers too.
   Zikky wikky mikky bee,
   Witchy witchy mitchy kee,
    Sikky tikky wee!

VII

Then, when so completely dressed,
Back they flew, and reached their nest.
Their children cried, "O ma and pa!
How truly beautiful you are!"
Said they, "We trust that cold or pain
We shall never feel again;
While, perched on tree or house or steeple,
We now shall look like other people.
 Witchy witchy witchy wee,
 Twikky mikky bikky bee,
 Zikky sikky tee!"